Scarface

a novel

by

PAUL KROPP

H·I·P Books

HIP Sr.

National Library of Canada Cataloguing in Publication Data

Kropp, Paul 1948–
[We both have scars]
    Scarface / Paul Kropp.

(New Series Canada)
Previously published under title: We both have scars.
ISBN 0-9731237-1-0

I. Title. II. Title: We both have scars. III. Series.

PS 8571.R772W4 2002   jC813'.54   C2002-90558-9
PZ7

General editor: Paul Kropp
Text Design: Laura Brady
Illustrations redrawn by: Matt Melanson
Cover design: Robert Corrigan

  ¯ 3 4 5 6 7   16 15 14 13 12 11

Printed and bound in Canada

High Interest Publishing acknowledges the financial support of the Government of Canada through the Canada Book Fund for our publishing activities

Coming to Canada had been a great thing for Tranh. This was a country of peace and wealth and happiness. So why did Martin Beamis keep picking on him? Did this rich guy have nothing better to do than make life rotten for someone who had already suffered so much?

CHAPTER 1

You Can Both Stop

Tranh and the bigger boy sat across from each other in the VP's office. Tranh sat up straight, trying to understand the words coming from Martin's mouth. The big kid leaned forward, staring at Mr. Watson. He seemed ready to pound his fist on the vice-principal's desk.

"I didn't start it," the kid went on, his voice booming. "The only reason I hit him was because he mouthed off to me. He's got a nasty mouth, this guy. They all do."

"That's enough!" Watson shot back. "I don't want any more talk about 'they' from you." His voice was angry. It reminded Tranh of the voice of a camp guard. "I'm just trying to find out what happened."

The vice-principal turned to Tranh and spoke

slowly. "Could you explain to me what happened?"

The vice-principal had grey skin and a red tie. His name was Watson but the students called him "Bonehead" because he was bald. The kids thought Watson was fair, but you had to watch out if he lost his temper.

"This guy called me Scarface," Tranh explained. "I don't even know him, and he uses that name."

"That's not true, sir," the loud boy broke in. "At least, only after he called me some name, some swear word in his language."

"And how would you know swearing in Cambodian?" Watson asked. "Are you an expert on language? Do you have any idea what he really said?" Watson was fuming as he sat behind his desk. "And even if he did, does that give you an excuse to pick on him? I mean, Tranh is just half your size."

Watson 's words were not exactly true, but close. If they had been standing, Martin would tower over Tranh. But he did not weigh twice as much. Tranh was short and muscular. He had grown strong in the refugee camps, just to survive.

"So then you jumped up and challenged him to

a fight," the vice-principal said.

"Well, yeah," the loud boy admitted.

Martin Beamis was built like a football player. He had long blond hair which would fall over his eyes unless he pushed it out of the way. His eyes were large and blue, his eyebrows were straight and his lower lip was very large. At this moment, both his lips were pushed out. And they were lying.

"You threatened to 'bust his head,' Martin. That's what it says here on Ms. Ballantyre's report." Watson leaned back in his chair. "Now tell me, do you think it's okay to challenge people to fights in English class?"

"Well, maybe not. But he called me a – "

"And you insulted him, didn't you?" Watson snapped back.

"I just called him what all the guys call him." Martin Beamis squirmed in his chair, his body too big for it. The kids at school really did call Tranh by the name 'Scarface,' but behind his back. The nickname fit, of course, because of the long scar beneath Tranh's right eye. But something about Tranh kept kids from saying the name to his face.

"Maybe 'all the guys' had better clean up their act," Watson told him. "Or I'll have 'all the guys' sitting in here with me."

Watson stared at Beamis, looking angry. He sat forward at his desk, pointing his pen as if it were a knife.

"I'm not going to have any of you and your buddies picking on someone of Tranh's size," Watson said.

Tranh spoke up. "They do not scare me," he said. His voice was cold. He had been in many fights back in the camp – real fights with knives and clubs and blood on the floor. He had learned how to look after himself. Tranh knew that speed and cunning worked better than size and muscle. He looked at Beamis and saw a boy who was fat, lazy and slow. He wasn't afraid.

"It was just a joke," Beamis said. "It didn't mean anything."

"According to Ms. Ballantyre's report, Martin, this was not the first time." Watson was reading the teacher's report. He needed glasses to see the print on the pink sheet in front of him. "She feels your attitude is creating racial tension in the class. She said you pick on Tranh and some of the other newcomers."

"That's crazy," Beamis said, turning away as if he were insulted.

"What do you think, Tranh?" Watson asked.

"I know that this guy calls me Scarface," Tranh told him. "He asks why I don't go back to my country. And he makes fun of me because my skin is not white, like his."

Beamis and Mr. Watson both stared at Tranh. Beamis was shaking his head, trying to pretend that this was a lie. Watson was angry. There was a deep crease in the skin between his eyes.

Tranh concluded, "All I know is that this fat boy likes to make jokes about me and some of my friends."

"Stop calling me 'fat boy,'" Beamis broke in.

"You can both stop!" Watson ordered, raising his voice. His face had turned pink, more like the color of his tie. "I've had enough of this," he lectured. Slowly he calmed down, and his face returned to its usual pale white. "I don't like your attitude, Martin.

I don't like the way you seem to bully the other kids in this school. I don't like the kinds of things you seem to say about people. I'm beginning to see why you had so much trouble at Ridley."

Ridley was a private school, a rich one. Beamis had been a student there until last year, but then he was "asked to leave." Though his father used both money and threats to try to keep him there, Ridley wanted him gone. Now he was in the public high school – and he hated it.

"But I'm going to give you a break," Watson went on. "I'm not going to call your father or give you a punishment." He stopped, waiting, staring at the rich boy. "*This* time," he concluded.

Beamis twisted in his seat. Tranh just looked straight ahead.

Watson went on, "But I don't want to get any more reports of this kind of thing. You know better, Martin. You know that Tranh has as much right to be here as you do. He has just as much right to find his way in this country as your grandparents did. You understand?"

"Yes, sir," Beamis said. He was lying again. He

looked at Tranh out of the corner of his eye. There was a little smile on his face, a smirk, as if this were all a game.

"And you, Tranh, have got to stop taking the bait. You can't insult people back when they call you names. Maybe the best thing is to ignore the stupid comments."

Tranh had heard this advice before, ever since he came here. Ignore the bullies, that's what the teachers always say. "Turn the other cheek." That's what it says in the Bible. But it was so hard to do that and keep your pride. So hard to listen to their words and deal with the hurt.

"Maybe you should try to join in a little more," Watson went on. "Play a sport at lunch time. Go on the next school trip. Try to fit in with some of the nice kids around here."

Tranh was silent. He didn't like the way the other students treated each other. They were loud and silly and insulting. Tranh was nineteen, older than all the other students in grade eleven. In terms of what he had been through, he was much, much older.

"Do you understand?"

"Yes," Tranh replied, turning his eyes away.

"Good," Watson concluded. "If I have to see either of you again, you'll be here for our breakfast club, understand? Now shake hands and get back to class."

Beamis put out his hand and smiled. He shook hands with Tranh as if the smaller boy were a long-lost friend. Then the two students went out the door together. Mr. Watson went back to the paperwork on his desk. He didn't see Martin Beamis reach out and touch Tranh on his shoulder. Nor could he hear the words that Beamis whispered.

"You're going to pay for this, you little dork."

CHAPTER 2

These Are Your Friends?

Tranh worked in his uncle's video store. His uncle's name was Tranh, too, but he called his store Mountain Video and DVD. He figured that it would get more customers than a store called "Tranh's Video." Even so, the store didn't get that much business. It was hard to compete against the big chain stores in the malls.

Still, Tranh felt lucky to be here and have a job. His uncle had sponsored him and made it possible to come to this new country. He had given him a place to live with his own family. Now he treated him like a son.

When Tranh was in the camps, waiting, he would get letters from his uncle. The letters would tell him about this new country. There were so many things that Tranh could not imagine: snow, cell phones, DVDs, homes where each child had a bedroom. In the refugee camps, Tranh had only a mat to sleep on. He ate mostly rice, but there was never enough. Sometimes the shipment of food would not come. Once, Tranh had eaten beetles to stay alive.

Now Tranh was here, working for his uncle at night, going to school during the day. His uncle urged him to go to school, "to get ahead" as the white people say.

Tranh felt he had already gotten ahead. His life was so much better than it had been in the camps. He'd been here only eight months, but this new world seemed to give him every chance.

"Your report card came in the mail," his uncle said as the old man rushed out of the store. "Your mother and father would be proud."

"I did not do so well in English," Tranh replied.

"You will get better," his uncle replied. "It takes time and practice."

Tranh had learned English in the camp, but it was very hard. He knew Cambodian from his village, French from his mother, and learned Thai

in the camp. But English was the hardest. So many words. So many exceptions to the rules. Then there was what Ms. Ballantyre called "shades of meaning." Tranh learned that even a simple word could mean many different things. It was so confusing, so hard to learn.

Tranh's uncle looked at his watch. "Can you look after the store while I go home? Lia is sick with some kind of flu. I'll be back in an hour or two."

"Of course," Tranh replied. He knew that his uncle worried about his family, and not just when they were ill. "Tuesday is always a slow night," Tranh told him. "I am fine on my own."

"All the stock is back on the shelves, the computer is working okay," his uncle said, going through a list in his mind. "If there is any problem – "

"I can handle it," Tranh said. "No problem."

Tranh liked these English phrases, the ones he did not learn in the camp. *No problem. Sure thing. Piece of cake, eh?* When he used them, he felt like he belonged here, like he had really found a home.

Tranh was alone, in the back of the store, when

they came in. He did not notice them at first. Then he heard Beamis' voice and turned to look.

He saw that Martin Beamis was not alone. There were five other boys with him. They were all big, all joking and laughing like they were drunk.

"Well, look who's here," Beamis said as Tranh moved to the front counter.

Tranh said nothing. His uncle had told him that "the customer is king" in this new country. His uncle had said, "the customer is always right," and Tranh tried hard to believe that. If Beamis was a customer, he must be treated well.

"It's Train Tracks," said one of Beamis' friends. That was another name they had given him in school. At least that one just made fun of his name, not his face.

"Better watch it," said one of the others, "or Train Tracks will report us to the vice-principal ."

"Nah, we can call him anything we want now," Beamis said. "There's nothing Watson can do to us outside school hours. Right, *Scarface?*"

Tranh turned his head so they could only see

the left side of his face, the good side. He kept his eyes down, trying to keep the anger inside.

"C'mon, Martin, let's get a DVD and get out of here," one of the boys said.

Beamis was smiling, but joined his friend at the back of the store. Another customer came in to return a video. Tranh took the return and scanned it into the computer.

When the customer left, Tranh saw Beamis and his friends back in the "Restricted" part of the store. They were looking at boxes of X-rated videos and DVDs.

"Hey, Tranh, you ever watch these?" one boy shouted.

"No," Tranh said. That was the truth. His uncle said those videos show no respect to women, or to men either. Still, the store had to stock them.

"How about we check out this one, Martin?" Jeff asked. He had an X-rated DVD in his hand.

"You must be eighteen," Tranh said.

"Suppose I tell you I *am* eighteen," Beamis said.

"I know you are not."

Beamis came over to the counter. "Scarface, I

wonder how someone as dumb as you ever got into this country."

Tranh stared at him but said nothing. His hands were trembling – not from fear, but from anger.

"So you won't let us take out any of these?" Jeff said. He ran his hand along one shelf and knocked down all the boxes. The other boys laughed.

"No," Tranh said. He had to grit his teeth and hold in his anger.

"Or these?" Beamis said. Then he did what his friend did, knocking down a whole shelf of boxes.

"I think you should leave the store," Tranh said. "We do not need your business."

"And I think you do," Beamis said, walking right over to him. "You know my father could buy and sell this place in two seconds flat. You'd be out on your duff so fast you wouldn't even know what happened."

"This is my uncle's store," Tranh replied. "He does not want to sell."

"Well isn't that nice," Beamis said, turning to his friends. "I guess these gooks are doing O.K., aren't they?"

"Taking over the whole country," one of them said.

"Taking all the decent jobs," said another.

"Even giving jobs to somebody like Scarface here," Beamis said. "It's like hiring the handicapped."

The others laughed, but Beamis did not. He was serious.

"I think it is time for you to leave," Tranh said again. He tried to stay polite, no matter what they did. His uncle had told him, you must always be polite.

"After we get a video or two," Beamis replied.

Quickly he stepped around the counter and pulled a DVD from the shelf behind Tranh's head. "Here, guys, I got the one we wanted."

"That's on reserve," Tranh told him. He reached out and grabbed Beamis' arm.

Beamis tried to pull free, but Tranh's grip was too strong. Beamis was surprised at the sudden pain in his wrist.

"Hey, gook, if you won't let go – " Beamis began, but he stopped when the door opened.

It was Tranh's uncle. He looked at the boxes on

19

the floor, then at Beamis behind the counter, then at Tranh.

"What's going on?" he said.

"Nothing," Beamis replied as Tranh let go of his arm.

"That's right," Jeff said. "Just a little friendly talk." All of them began to move toward the door. "Looks like your guy here doesn't want our business."

Tranh's uncle looked at them all. He did not know what to say. But he saw that the big blond kid and his friends were heading to the door.

"See you in school," Beamis called as he went out the door, "*Scarface.*"

"Gook!" added Jeff as they headed out to their car. "Two gooks!" The others laughed. For them, all this had been a joke.

When their car roared off, Tranh's uncle looked at him. "These are your friends?" he asked.

"No," Tranh replied. "Not friends, but I know them from school."

"Sometimes I wonder," his uncle said, "what they teach in schools that boys should act like that."

"The schools don't teach them to hate," Tranh said, thinking of Mr. Watson. "They just cannot stop them from being stupid."

CHAPTER 3

Back to the Office

Over the next few weeks, Beamis would not leave Tranh alone. He treated the smaller student the way a cat teases a mouse. One day Tranh's lock was taken from his locker. Everything was gone. The next day, everything was back, but there was "gook" – and worse words – written on his books.

Beamis and his friends made jokes when Tranh would pass by. "Seen any good movies?" Beamis would ask, and the others laugh. "Ah, he's just a little gook," said Jeff. Tranh pretended not to hear, but his pride was hurt by the jokes and insults.

Fortunately, Beamis was in only one of his classes. The two of them both took grade ten English with Ms. Ballantyre. In the English class, they studied grammar and short stories and Shakespeare. Tranh was good at grammar – better than Beamis even in this third language – but Shakespeare was hard for everyone.

Beamis made jokes as the class tried to read *The Merchant of Venice*. He made jokes about Jews and Italians and Tranh, too. As if Shakespeare had ever heard of Cambodia. But Beamis liked to get attention from the kids, and from the teacher. One way was to make jokes and act like an idiot.

Beamis would find lots of hidden ways to pick on Tranh in class. Most were small – stealing his pen, stepping on his foot, dropping food on his papers. But what made it all worse was that this all happened in front of a girl.

Jasmine. Among all the white faces in Tranh's class, there was one brown face like his. Except, of course, that Jasmine's face was perfect. Her skin was soft and smooth. Her hair was long, dark and shiny. Like Tranh, she was from Southeast Asia. When she smiled, Tranh could only think of the flower that was her name.

Still, Tranh was too shy to speak to her very much. Perhaps she liked him, but only as a friend.

Perhaps if Tranh did not have this scar on his face . . .
Perhaps if Tranh were a little richer, or more sure of
himself . . .

"What happened to your books, Tranh?"
Jasmine asked one day.

"Someone broke into my locker," he replied.
Tranh knew very well who had done it, but he had
no proof. "This was how they came back."

"Ms. Ballantyre will have a fit," she said. Jasmine
has been here for many years, and spoke like all the
other students.

It took twenty minutes before Jasmine's words
came true. It was "free reading time," and Ms.
Ballantyre walked up and down the rows, holding
her pointer. She stopped at Tranh's desk.

"What happened to your books, Tranh?" she
asked.

"They were stolen," he said. The rest of the class
pretended to read, but they were watching him.
Tranh felt ashamed for something that was not
his fault.

"And the thief decorated your books?" she

asked. On one book was written "THE TANK" with a sketch of Ms. Ballantyre.

"Yes."

"Someone stole your books, and marked up the covers, and gave them back. You expect me to believe that?"

"That was what happened," Tranh told her, because it was the truth.

Someone in the class laughed. Ms. Ballantyre looked around the room, her face like a hawk's.

"This isn't funny," she told the class. "There is no learning without books. And there is certainly no learning when some of you behave like children."

She turned back to Tranh. "I think you should go down to the office and explain this to the vice-principal. Maybe Mr. Watson – "

As she said his name, Beamis whispered "Bonehead" to Jeff. But the class heard it and began to laugh.

"Another joke, Mr. Beamis?" she said. "Is there any person in this school who escapes your rude humor?"

"No, ma'am," Beamis said, and some students laughed. "I mean, I was just clearing my throat." He coughed several times.

"Perhaps you have some idea what happened to Tranh's books?" she said.

"No, ma'am. I certainly do not. I think it's shocking that Tranh would draw a picture making fun of you on his books." Beamis grinned.

"The lettering, Martin, isn't in Tranh's writing," the teacher told him. "In fact, the handwriting looks a lot like yours."

"What, me? Are you accusing . . ." Beamis began as if he had done nothing.

Ms. Ballantyre frowned. "Martin, I think you, too, should go to the office," she said. There was a murmur in the class. "Tranh can explain about his books. And you can tell Mr. Watson about your cough. Maybe you can explain why your cough sounds so much like a certain rude nickname." She looked over the classroom, to see if anyone else might dare laugh now. But the class was silent.

"But ma'am – " Beamis protested.

"To the office, *now*," she shouted. "Both of you."

Tranh got up as the whole class watched. He could feel Jasmine's eyes following him, and he felt ashamed. Why was this happening to him?

Outside Mr. Watson's office was a hard wooden bench. Beamis and Tranh sat at opposite ends of the bench.

Tranh sometimes wondered if he should stay in school. He was older than the others, old enough to work, save money and start his own business. But his uncle said he should finish high school. He said that Tranh was smart, and should go on to college. "So you can get a good job," his uncle said. "So you can be more than a shopkeeper." Tranh asked him what was so bad about running a store. His uncle just looked at him, with more pity than anger. "Because you can do more, Tranh. Your mother would want you to do all that you can."

But school was not easy. Most of the students were white. Many of them treated Tranh like an outsider, like someone who didn't belong. They looked at him and saw only Scarface, Train Tracks, the "little gook." Tranh tried to laugh it off, to ignore the whispers and the insults, but it was hard.

And then there was Beamis, who made it all worse.

When Mr. Watson opened the door and saw them, he was already red-faced and angry.

"You two!" he shouted.

"Sir – " Beamis began, but Mr. Watson was not listening.

"I thought I told you two I never wanted to see your faces down here again." He ripped the pink referral sheet from Beamis's hands.

"From Ms. Ballantyre's class. Again!" he shouted. He had not even read the paper.

The secretaries in the office were watching all this. One of them was smiling, as if it were a joke. But Tranh knew it was serious. He felt ashamed to be here.

"Martin, I should suspend you right now," he shouted. "But I'm going to give you one last chance. You and your friend, here."

Tranh looked up. Did Mr. Watson really think he was Beamis's friend?

"I want both of you down here tomorrow morning. Seven-thirty. Seven-thirty a.m.," Watson repeated, drawing out the "aaay-ehmm."

"I can explain – " Beamis said.

"Tomorrow morning you can explain all you want," Watson said. "Both of you. And let me remind you two jokers that this is your last chance. If you're late, or don't show up, you're *gone*."

Beamis looked stunned.

Mr. Watson suddenly smiled at the two of them. "Congratulations, gentlemen. You both just joined the Breakfast Club."

CHAPTER 4

The Breakfast Club

It was 7:25. There were six of them gathered for the "Breakfast Club," but there was no breakfast. The students watched each other while Mr. Watson watched the clock, waiting. No one spoke.

Under the clock was a small boy, smaller than Tranh. The kids called him "Iggie" though his real name was Ignacius. He was dressed in a tough style – plaid shirt over a black T-shirt, marked-up jeans, leather boots – but his face was scared. It was as if his tough clothes covered up a frightened soul.

Next to him sat Beamis. He wore a T-shirt and tan pants that were rolled up. He was smiling at the girl to his right, a girl who called herself "Buffy," though her real name was Sheila. The girl had hair with five different colors in it. The hair seemed to stand straight up in some places, fall over her face in other spots. Buffy wore a leather jacket with shiny studs, and she would not take it off though the office was very hot.

There were two boys next to Buffy who seemed to be friends. One was very, very, tall, and the other was short and fat. The tall one, Andrew, wore three or four shirts under his leather jacket. Five earrings dangled from his right ear; six from his left.

His short friend, Mike, had glasses that were taped together. He wore mostly ripped clothing and scuffed boots. His jacket smelled like rotten milk.

And there was Tranh. Tranh was angry at having to be here. He knew it was Beamis who should be punished, but Watson didn't understand. So this morning Tranh had to sneak from his uncle's house early. If his uncle knew of this, he'd be too upset and ashamed.

The group waited. It was 7:29 when they heard someone running down the hall. When the door opened, they saw the final member of the Breakfast Club.

Jasmine!

Tranh was stunned. He couldn't imagine a girl

like Jasmine getting into trouble. She said so little in class. She just smiled and laughed, a wonderful laugh that seemed like music to Tranh. Yet she was here.

"Just in time, Miss Ling," Mr. Watson said as he closed the door.

Jasmine sat down next to Tranh, still out of breath from her run. Tranh felt her arm touch his as she tried to get her breath. It was trembling. Neither of them could look at the other.

"Welcome to the club, kids," Mr. Watson said. He looked at each of them in turn, smiling as if this were some kind of game. "Each of you has done something stupid or anti-social to join the club," Mr. Watson said.

Tranh saw that there was dried egg yolk on his tie. At least Mr. Watson had had his breakfast.

"Some of you already know the routine. What I want to hear, from each of you, was what you did to end up here. That way we get all our problems right out front." His smile was forced, as if he had been through this too many times. "Andrew, you begin. You know what to do."

The huge boy looked at the ceiling and shook his head. Then he spoke in a strange, high-pitched voice, "I told Mr. Martin he was a goof. He bugged me because of the way I look, but I guess I still shouldn't have called him a goof. So, I'm sorry, kind of. A little."

Watson nodded his head and turned to Mike. "I feel that I am falsely accused," the fat boy said.

"Save it until you're a lawyer," Watson snapped at him. "Let's hear it."

Mike groaned and began his story, "Ms. Marker said I stole money from her purse."

"And." Watson prompted him.

"And I didn't steal it. It was just a loan, kind of, but she didn't know about it."

The other kids laughed and Andrew said "Suuure!" while hitting Mike with his elbow.

Mike made a strange face. "All right, so I guess it was stupid, and anti-social, so I'm sorry."

"Sheila?" Watson asked.

"Buffy," she corrected him.

"O.K., so it's Buffy this week. Let's hear your story."

"Like I was bugging this girl," Buffy said. "That one, the little chick over there. But then she started giving me a hard time. . ."

"Cut it, Buffy," Watson told her. "Jasmine can tell her own story. What have *you* got to say?"

Buffy shook her multi-colored hair and looked at him. "Like, I'm sorry. It was dumb."

"Thank you," Watson replied. "It's a pleasure to have you join us. Now you, Iggie."

The little guy began. "This meatball was leaning on me, so I slugged him. And I guess I shouldn't have, so I'm sorry. Kind of."

Watson shook his head, but kept on going around the circle. "Martin – "

"I . . . well, somebody wrote on this guy's books," Beamis said, pointing to Tranh. "And I got blamed for it, so here I am."

"But you didn't do it?" Watson asked.

"Not me," Beamis replied. "I wouldn't do something like that. Maybe I pick on guys in some other ways, but I wouldn't do something as stupid as *that*," he said.

The others smiled because they knew he was

lying. Beamis had already bragged to half the school about what he'd done. Not even Watson was fooled, but the VP went on, turning to Jasmine.

"And you, Jasmine?"

Tranh could not bear to look at the girl. He felt embarrassed for her, and for himself. Here they

were, together, in trouble, ashamed. Surely she could not deserve this punishment either.

"I did a stupid thing," Jasmine began. Her voice, unlike the others, was trembling. "I got really mad when Buffy was bothering me in Family Studies, so . . ."

"So what did you do?" Iggie asked.

"I threw food in her face," Jasmine whispered.

Buffy jumped up and angrily pointed her finger at Jasmine. "A pie! She stuck a —ing pie right in my face!"

"Clean it up!" Watson ordered. He and Buffy stared at each other until Watson turned his eyes away.

"I'm sorry," Jasmine said at last. "It was wrong . . . " and then she began to cry.

The group grew strangely quiet. They watched Jasmine cry, perhaps the only real emotion so far in the morning.

Tranh listened to the sound of her crying – the rasping breath, the awful tone in the back of her throat. He thought of his mother and his grandmother. There had been so much crying, so many tears in his life. If only men were allowed to cry, he thought, it would be better. After his father was killed, he had become the man in their house. He could not cry, or show weakness, or they would kill him too. He had to be strong, for the little ones. For his brother and sister. For all the lost ones.

"O.K.," Watson said, clearing his throat, "let's keep going. You, Tranh – "

"I am not sure," he began. "Ms. Ballantyre sent me to the office because someone wrote on my books."

"That's not your problem," Watson said. "Not your real problem."

Tranh just looked at him with a question in his eyes.

"Maybe you're here to find out what your real problem is, Tranh." Watson looked at him strangely, as if he knew something that Tranh had not figured out.

Maybe I am here unjustly, Tranh thought to himself, but he did not speak. In his country, it was forbidden to talk back to a teacher.

"All right, let's get going," Watson went on. "I

think a few of you could stand to know each other a bit better than you do. So I'm breaking you up into groups of two. You're going to write a biography of two hundred words on the other guy. You know what a biography is, Iggie?"

"I'm not that dumb, sir. It's like the real story of somebody's life," Iggie told him.

"You got it," Watson said. "You guys take notes today, then you write over the weekend. Find out where your partner comes from, his family, his home life. Do a real good job and you won't have to be in the club any more."

"But I like it here, sir," Andrew said. "It's a lot nicer than waking up and having to look at my mother."

"Andrew," Watson said, "that's really touching. Your reward is that you get to team up with me. Iggie and Mike – you're a team. Buffy and Jasmine – you two work together. And that leaves Martin and Tranh. Find a corner of the room to work in. See if you can get to know another human being. For some of you, it might be the first time."

Watson got up and took Andrew into his office.

Buffy and Jasmine went off to a corner, Buffy still grumbling to herself. Iggie and Mike took two seats under a book shelf. Beamis got up and moved to a desk by the file cabinet. He sat down in a big, tilting chair. This left only a filing stool for Tranh to sit upon.

Beamis had a smirk on his face even as Tranh sat down. "O.K., *Tranh*," he began, "I'm supposed to get to know you as a human being. Now tell me how you got the scar."

CHAPTER 5

Two Families

Tranh said nothing. The two of them sat there for five minutes, staring at each other, silent. Finally Mr. Watson came by and said that one of them had better start talking, fast.

So Tranh began. "My country was Cambodia," he said. He wondered if Beamis could spell the word, but did not offer to help. "It is a very beautiful country – very warm, with flowers beside the roads. My family lived in a small town on a river and my father was the – I think your word is 'mayor.'"

Beamis looked up. Perhaps he was impressed, but Tranh was not sure.

"The people were very happy until an army came, the Khmer Rouge. They came and raided the towns, killing anyone who would not support them. At first, we tried to fight back. But the Khmer

Rouge had guns and then bombs. We had only knives. My father was an important man in our village." Tranh's voice trailed off. He remembered those times. He remembered the day his cousin came running in with the news, and then his mother's tears.

"So what happened?" Beamis asked.

"They killed him." Tranh tried to make his voice cold, as if he no longer cared.

Beamis wrote it down. He had stopped smiling.

Tranh continued, "My family had to escape. My mother took what she could and tried to go south. But the roads had mines, the bombs that explode when you walk on them. We had to walk through the jungle sometimes. There was nothing to eat and sometimes the water made us sick. Then, one night, my mother was fishing in a pond, and the soldiers found us." Tranh paused as he remembered. He was not going to tell Beamis everything. This boy did not deserve the whole terrible story.

"They took us to a town and made us work in the rice fields," Tranh went on. "That was where I grew up. First we were in my country, then we were moved to a second camp in Thailand. And then we escaped."

"So how'd you get out?" Beamis asked.

"We paid a man to get us on a boat to the Philippines. He said that there we would be safe. So we snuck out of the camp at night and got on the boat. It was a small boat – a junk, they call it – but there were sixty people crowded on the deck. There were four of us – my mother, my little brother, my sister, and me."

Tranh became silent. He could never forget that night, the full moon shining off the water. None of them could speak or even breathe for fear of being found out. There were all those people on the boat, the stink of fear and sweat, and the still moon over the water.

"So what happened?" Beamis asked.

Tranh came out of his memory. Suddenly it felt too strange, telling all this to a stranger. Beamis had no right to know more. Tranh had not even told the whole story to his uncle. This white boy would not be the first to hear it.

So he rushed through all the rest. "We were

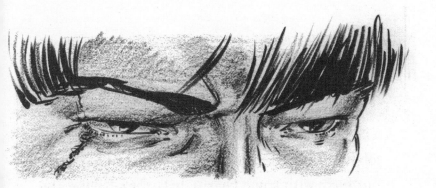

attacked by pirates. Many people in the boat died, but I was rescued and brought here."

"Pretty wild," Beamis said. He had forgotten about the scar and seemed more serious than before. Perhaps Watson was right. Perhaps knowing each other would help.

"Now I must write about you," Tranh told him. His pen was ready but he did not know what to ask.

Beamis began without even a question. "Well, my old man has a lot of money. That's why I went to Ridley. It made my parents look good."

"So you admire your father?" Tranh asked.

Beamis laughed. "My father's got lots of money but not much time, if you know what I mean. I see him maybe once a week, if he can fit me in between cases. And then it's push, push, push. How come I haven't got straight A's? How come I'm not *captain* of the football team? It's like whatever I do just isn't good enough for the old man."

"And your mother?" Tranh asked.

"Oh, she's your perfect society wife. Her whole job is to keep everything looking good. When she's not busy with some charity ball, she's having tea with some big shot's wife. And sometimes she has to worry a little about me."

"Why is that?"

"Because I'm not the perfect little boy I'm supposed to be. I mean, I was supposed to be born wearing a blue-striped tie. I was supposed to study hard, be good and go straight to Harvard. Except it didn't work out. I kept getting bounced out of private schools. I got into fights. I was pretty good at sports – hockey, skiing, that kind of thing. But I wouldn't wear my tie pushed up the way they wanted. I suppose I caused my parents lots of problems." Beamis had a strange smile on his face, as if he were proud of this.

"Anyway, I couldn't hack it with the private school thing. So now I'm stuck here. My father had a fit when they tossed me out of Ridley. Went right off the deep end, but I didn't care."

"Deep end?"

"Yeah, it means he went nuts, like crazy," Beamis explained.

"You brought disgrace to your family?" Tranh asked. He was as amazed by this as Beamis had been at his story.

"Nah. My family *is* a disgrace. It's just that nobody can see it. If you've got enough money in this country, no one can see what you're really like."

Tranh was still trying to write all this down when Watson told them their time was up. It was 8:40 and a secretary had come in. She stood beside Watson, who was frowning as he spoke.

"O.K., breakfast club members. Time's up. You get to talk more tomorrow if you need it, then I want these in on Monday."

"Monday!" Andrew said. "You mean I've got to work on this over the weekend?"

"You better," Watson replied, "or don't bother coming back to this school." Then he grinned.

"Besides, I've got a little surprise for you guys on Winter Sports Day next week."

"Like what?" Iggie said.

"Like skiing," Watson said. "The Rotary Club has kicked in some money so a few extra kids can go skiing. I've signed the seven of you up. I told them you were all disadvantaged."

"What's that mean?" Iggie asked.

"It means *poor*, stupid," Mike told him. "It means we're social rejects."

"Hey, I can pay for my own skiing," Beamis said.

"And so you can, Martin," Watson replied. "You and Jasmine can pay your own way. For the rest of you – better thank the Rotary Club. Maybe a day at Mount Seymour will be just what you all need. Maybe you'll learn something about getting along with each other. And who knows, maybe you'll even learn how to ski before you crash into a tree."

Beamis called out, "I was on the ski team at my last school."

"That doesn't surprise me," Watson replied. "So you'll be just the person to help out some of the kids who can't ski. How many of you have ever skied before?" he asked, looking at the rest of them.

No one raised a hand.

"Wonderful," Watson said, hitting his bald head with one hand. "Then let me give you the bad news. I'm going to teach you all how to do it. And if even one of you gives me trouble, or mouths off, you'll be eating snow for the whole day."

CHAPTER 6

Skiing Mount Seymour

The wind was cold, even at the bottom of Mt. Seymour. The seven members of the Breakfast Club were standing on a little rise near the ski rental hut. The other students, the ones who had paid for the trip, were off on the hill.

Mr. Watson had watched them get ready. He wondered how this experiment of his would go. Maybe a day on the ski slope would be as good as a week at Outward Bound. Maybe it would teach these kids a thing or two.

When the kids had managed to get on their boots, Mr. Watson lined them up near the ski lodge.

"You start by learning how to fall down," Watson said. Then he walked up to Andrew and gave him a shove.

"Hey, man!" Andrew shouted as he fell over. Then each of them, except Beamis, got a push that sent them falling to the snow.

They looked up from the snow to see Watson and Beamis grinning. For them, this was a game.

"You'll probably do a lot of falling today, so we'll start by teaching you how to get up. Watch Martin," Watson said, pushing him down.

Beamis fell on his back, still grinning. Then he stuck the end of one ski in the snow, moved the other ski over, and pushed himself up. It seemed so easy.

"The trick," said Watson, "is to use the hill. Get your skis so they're pointing across the hill, not up or down. That's it. And then use the slope of the hill to help you up."

Tranh did what he said and pushed himself up. Mike and Iggie were laughing, but helped each other up. Buffy was swearing, but they all got back on their skis. Only Jasmine had trouble, and Beamis pulled her up with his hand.

When he touched her, Tranh felt an ache in his heart. He was jealous. Without any reason, without any hope of her approval, he was jealous.

"Now I'm going to teach you the snowplow," Watson said. "The snowplow isn't the fastest way to get down the hill, but it works and gives you control. Remember that when you ski – you always stay in control. Now watch Martin."

Beamis had gone up to the top of the rise. He was dressed in a bright blue and white ski suit. When Mike asked him, Beamis said the outfit cost seven hundred dollars. Then he complained about having to use old skis because his own were getting new bindings.

Tranh shook his head. In his country, a person did not make seven hundred dollars in a full year of work. Yet here people are so rich, and they still complain.

Tranh wore pajamas under his jeans, and a garbage bag in between to stay dry. But still the wind whistled through his jacket and gloves. It was cold up on the mountain, way below freezing.

Andrew shivered, but he would not button up his leather jacket. Nor would Iggie put on a hat. Only Jasmine and Beamis were dressed for this.

Jasmine's family had been in Vancouver for ten

years – and they had done well. So she wore a bright pink ski suit that seemed to glow in the sun. Her gloves were expensive, with many layers to keep her hands warm. But Jasmine could not ski. All these wonderful clothes and she had never been on a ski hill.

"Pay attention, Tranh," Watson shouted. "To do the snowplow, you put your skis into a V and push against the snow. The more you push, the slower you go. Show 'em, Martin."

Beamis glided down the hill as if skiing were nothing at all.

"Now we're all going to try it," Watson yelled out. "Get your skis in a V – but don't let the tips touch. That's it."

Tranh turned and faced down the little slope. He gave a push with the poles and began to slide – slowly, slowly, then faster, then he pushed out to slow down. He felt like a one year-old learning to walk, but it worked.

Jasmine skied down beside him. She was doing fine until the end, when her skis crossed. Then, suddenly, she fell to one side and both skis came flying off. When Tranh got to her, she was laughing.

"I did it!" she said.

"You were wonderful," he told her. Tranh gave
her his hand to help her up. He wanted to help her
with her skis, but Beamis was already there. He was

busy brushing snow off Jasmine, as if she couldn't do it herself.

"O.K., you ski pros, let's all try it again," Watson shouted.

And they did. They trudged up the hill, skied down, fell down, got up and then learned how to turn.

Soon Tranh had forgotten about the cold and the wind that was blowing across the snow. He thought that skiing was fun. When Watson told them to line up for the chair lift, Tranh was first in line.

Tranh became scared when the chair lift was only halfway up the hill. Mt. Seymour is high, very high. The motor of the chair lift was noisy. Tranh tried to remember what Mr. Watson had said. Keep your skis straight and push off when you get to the top. Then stop and wait, Watson had said.

"Pretty awesome, eh?" Iggie asked as they rode up. He was Tranh's partner for the day.

"Yes, it is," Tranh replied.

"I'm a little scared," Iggie said, though his words were like a question.

"I have been more scared," Tranh told him. And that was true. But he had never been scared in quite this way.

"You ready, guy?" Iggie asked, lifting the safety bar.

Tranh pushed forward in the seat, trying to get ready. The chair seemed to push him forward at the very end, and he went sliding down and to the right.

Iggie didn't do quite so well. He pushed off too soon and fell into the snow. The lift stopped and someone went out to help him up.

Tranh joined Jasmine and Buffy down near a map of the ski hill. Only then could he look around, and only then did he realize how high up they were. Suddenly he was very, very afraid.

So was Jasmine. "I can't do this," she said. Her teeth were chattering, but not from the cold.

"Don't be a jerk," Buffy told her. But she, too, was just waiting at the top.

"We're going down *there?*" Iggie asked when he skied up beside them.

Andrew and Mike came off the lift, but Mike

fell down halfway to where the rest were waiting.

"Man, I think Watson is trying to kill us," Andrew said.

"I think this is a cruel punishment," Mike whined, "and should be forbidden under the Charter . . ."

"Oh, shut up," Andrew told him. "You're fat enough to roll down this mountain. It's the rest of us who are in trouble."

Finally Mr. Watson came off the chair lift with Martin Beamis at his side. The two of them skied down to the group very fast. Beamis did a quick turn to stop, spraying snow on the others.

"Hey, goof," Iggie shouted.

Watson stepped between the two of them before a real fight could start. He wore a ski toque over his bald head and a fancy ski jacket. It seemed clear that Watson had been skiing for many years.

Watson looked at the members of the Breakfast Club. "Not bad for beginners," he told them. "Now you get your first real skiing. We're going down the mountain, all the way."

"Down there?" Andrew asked.

Mike was not happy either. "Mr. Watson, I want to launch a protest. I think you've – "

"Protest all you want," Watson told him. "It gets really cold protesting up here overnight. Better to shut your mouth and use your skis. The only way down is by skiing down. Unless you break a leg – then they send a helicopter."

"Hey, Mike's fat enough to roll down there," Andrew said, grinning.

"He'd be a huge snowball when he got to the bottom," Iggie added.

Their jokes were enough to make Mike fall silent. Tranh looked down the hill and, like the others, he was scared. But there were hundreds of skiers making their way down the hill. If they could do it, so could Tranh.

"Martin, you start us off," Watson said. "Real slow, a few wide turns. We'll all stop just before that black marker."

Beamis nodded and began down the hill. He did five turns using the snowplow, then came to an easy stop by the marker.

"You're next, Tranh," Watson ordered. "So far, you've done real well."

Tranh could feel Jasmine's eyes watching him. He wanted to do this well, wanted to ski as well as Martin Beamis.

So he pushed off, skiing down for a while, then to the left, then to the right. He tried to follow the track that Beamis had made, tried to bend forward and keep his balance.

He was doing well until he hit a patch of ice. Then he started going faster, out of control, until he hit snow again. Carefully, he pushed out into the snowplow to slow down. He was almost to the black marker. *How did Watson say to stop?* he wondered.

Tranh remembered. He pushed with his left leg, hard, harder. Then he was somehow pointing up the hill – and he was stopped.

"Not bad," Beamis told him, and Tranh smiled.

He waved at the others to come after him, and they did. First Iggie, then Mike, then Jasmine when Buffy pushed her, then Buffy and Andrew.

"Hey, man, it's not so bad. We made it this far," Iggie said as he skied up next to Tranh.

But it was not so easy for Jasmine. She fell, once, twice, and then Watson had to help her up. And it was hard for Andrew, too. He was so tall and so awkward on the skis, but somehow he didn't fall down.

So the Breakfast Club skied down Mount Seymour, a bit at a time. Each of them fell once or twice or three times, but they learned to laugh and get up on their skis. Slowly they got closer to the base of the hill. Closer to the ski lodge, where Buffy said she would buy them all hot chocolate.

At the end, it was Andrew who pushed ahead of Beamis to get to the lodge first. He yelled as he sailed down the slope. Then Mike and Iggie and Buffy went by. They screamed out, "Hey – it's the Breakfast Club," until Mike fell down and came rolling to a stop.

But Tranh was not in a hurry. He held back on the hill, waiting for Jasmine to finish each section of skiing. She's so scared, he thought to himself. Someone has to be with her.

When they finally made it to the bottom, Jasmine and Tranh were side by side.

"We've come a long way," Tranh said.

"Yes," she replied, turning her eyes away. "Yes, we have."

CHAPTER 7

Trail Closed

Tranh decided that he liked this new sport, this sport called skiing. There was something about sailing down these hills, the snow spraying up, the wind blowing in his face. In Cambodia, he did not have the snow or the cold. He had had heat, hunger and war. And now this, this wonderful new country.

He felt lucky to be out here, on this mountain, with these people. Iggie told him that he was "a natural." Jasmine kept looking at him with admiration in her eyes. Knowing that she was watching, Tranh tried to do more. Parallel turns. Stem Christies. None of this seemed very hard to him.

Of course, Beamis did a lot of showing off too. He did crazy jumps, skied off the side of the trail, zoomed down the toughest trails.

"The jerk thinks he's on TV," Iggie said.

"He's always showing off," Mike said. Then he went on in a German accent. "Iz based on deep-seated insecurity, ya?"

The rest of them laughed. This had been a good morning for the Breakfast Club. They had taken on a challenge, and won. Now they had learned to count on each other, to joke about who they are. Tranh thought to himself, *these are my friends.*

All day they skied, and had a good time on the easy trails: Goldie and Easy-Does-It. Slowly they got better and faster. By three o'clock, when the snow started falling, even Buffy was laughing. No one in school had seen her laugh before.

"I'm a ski-Buffy," she said, giggling like a little girl.

The rest of them laughed with her. Even Mike, who had spent more time falling than skiing. Even Andrew, who had lost two earrings someplace on the hill.

Tranh spent most of his day with Jasmine, though they did not talk much at first. After lunch, it was Jasmine who spoke to him, smiling more

now that she was less afraid. Her words fell on Tranh's ears like music, beautiful music.

Jasmine was laughing with Tranh when Beamis came skiing over.

"So who's ready for a real hill?" Beamis asked. He was bragging even in the question.

"Lay off it, man," Andrew told him.

"Yeah, we're beginners," Mike said. "We're here to ski, not to commit suicide."

Beamis stared at him, then turned to Tranh. "What about you, Tranh? You think you're ready to get off the easy trails?"

"I don't know," he replied. But Jasmine was watching him with those dark eyes. Perhaps that was why he got boastful. "I think so."

"Sure he is," said Iggie. "He's only been skiing a day, but he's already as good as you are."

"What about it?" Beamis asked him. "Are you really as good as these guys think?"

Tranh knew, even then, that he should have backed off. He could have said, "Take a hike," or "I'm happy right here with the others." But he felt he had to prove himself, especially in front of Jasmine.

"All right," he said. "I'll try."

"We'll go up the other lift and try Unicorn Trail," Beamis told him. "Beat the moguls on that, and you can say you're a real skier."

"You show him, Tranh," Iggie called out. "Show this hot dog that he's not all that great."

Tranh and Beamis skied beyond the lodge to a second chair lift. The lift went up to a different part of the mountain. Soon the chair came to scoop the two of them up in the air.

At the top, Beamis skied off to the left while the other people went right, down the hill. Tranh followed behind Beamis to the sign that marked the Unicorn Trail. But today there was a second sign: TRAIL CLOSED.

"We can't go this way," Tranh told him.

"So what?" Beamis said. "You going to let a sign stop you? I'm willing to try it. Don't tell me you're chicken."

Tranh shook his head. He knew he was not "chicken" as these people would say. He knew he was brave in ways that they would never know. But he was not sure what to do next.

"I'll go first and show you the way. I mean, if you're really a hotshot skier like Jasmine thinks . . ."

His words died out, but the meaning was clear. If Tranh backed away, Martin would tell Jasmine and the others that he had "chickened out."

Tranh checked the map and saw that the trail wouldn't be too hard. It was a blue trail on the map. Besides, he told himself, it would be just once. Just one run down the hill, and then he could go back with his friends.

"All right," he said. "But the two of us go *together*." Then he pushed off, slid around the snow fence, and took the lead.

Beamis soon passed him, but by now the trail had gotten narrow and the two of them had to ski in a single line. There was fog around them, but both of them kept skiing fast. The trees on either side of the trail were a blur as they sailed down the hill.

This was crazy, Tranh knew, but it felt good to go racing down the hill like this. Fast. Faster. There was no time to think of anything except the snow and the skis and. . . .

The ice.

Suddenly the trail was all ice. Tranh lost any kind of control. He slid all over the ice, faster and faster as the hill fell away. He made a snowplow with his skis and pushed out. Nothing happened. He was going too fast, way too fast to turn or stop or do anything except . . .

Sit down.

That's what Watson said. "If you really get in trouble, sit down."

As he sat, the skis flew off his boots. Then his poles seemed to be ripped from his hands. And then Tranh was falling, falling and rolling.

But then, somehow, he stopped. Tranh sat up and looked around at the dirty snow.

But Tranh was not the only one who had fallen. Someplace down below him, in the fog, there was a scream. The cry cut through the foggy air, sharper than the groans that followed.

"Beamis!" Tranh shouted into the cold air.

But there was no answer. Someplace down below there was the sound of pain, the cries of someone who's been hurt – and hurt bad.

CHAPTER 8

The Scar

Beamis was crying when Tranh got to him. He was holding his leg in his gloved hands and swearing, over and over.

"Tranh, you gotta help me," he said, his voice full of pain.

"How are you hurt?" Tranh asked. The smaller boy could see blood on Beamis' face, but the pain was not there.

"It's my leg," Beamis said. "I broke my – " He tried to stretch out the leg, then cried out as the pain struck again. "I can't stand it!" he said. His breath was coming fast. It made a cloud of steam in front of his face.

"I can go to get help," Tranh told him.

For a moment Beamis said nothing. They both

looked down the mountain to where the trail disappeared in the fog.

Beamis's blue eyes were frightened. "No," he said, "It'll take too long." His face tightened up with pain. "They'll send someone when we're not back."

"Maybe I can get to the lodge faster and get help," Tranh replied. He reached for his ski poles and began to get up, as if ready to leave.

"No!" Beamis shrieked. He stared at Tranh like a madman, then grabbed at the smaller boy's arm. "I . . . I don't want to be out here . . . alone."

Tranh looked down at him, at this very big boy who was so frightened by his pain. Where was Martin Beamis' courage now? Tranh thought. What happened to the noisy show off who could take on anything?

But Tranh knew the feeling of fear in Beamis' heart. He, too, had been hurt and alone and afraid. He knew, better than anyone, that there was nothing worse.

"So I will stay," Tranh told him. "We will wait here together until help comes."

The two of them sat silently in the wet, heavy air. It was even colder and darker on this side of the mountain. The fog was thick now and the sun was going down. Soon it would be dark and the two of them would be alone, lost, on the frozen mountain.

Beamis had begun to shake, from pain or fear or both.

"It's not so bad," Tranh told him. He was trying to make him feel better, but his words couldn't do enough.

"It was stupid," Beamis spat out, "so stupid to do the trail in this fog!"

"You were showing off," Tranh said. "Sometimes that makes a person do stupid things."

Beamis shook his head and looked down at his gloves. "I should know, really. Sometimes I think I've spent my whole stupid life showing off. I feel like I always have to prove myself to somebody. I gotta be smarter, or braver or crazier. You know?"

Tranh nodded his head, though he wasn't sure he really understood.

"So if you know this, why do you do it?" Tranh asked him.

For a while, Beamis was silent. He stared out into the woods around them, into the fog. Then some quiet words came from his lips, "It's because of my old man."

Tranh looked at Beamis, a question in his eyes.

"He only had one kid – me – so I always had to do everything. I had to be the best skier and the fastest swimmer and the smartest kid. But it never worked. I could never be exactly what he wanted." Beamis was having trouble as he spoke. The tears would not stop falling down his cheeks. When he coughed, his whole body jumped in pain.

"Can you be what *you* want?" Tranh asked him.

"I don't *know* what I want," Beamis said bitterly.

Tranh shivered as the cold wind blew through his jacket. Now that he had stopped moving, he could really feel the freezing air.

"You're talking too much," Tranh told him. "You should rest so the bleeding will stop." The skin on his cheek had been cut by a rock, but now blood came only from the edge of his mouth.

Beamis pulled off his glove and reached up to touch his face. He felt the edge of the scrape, then

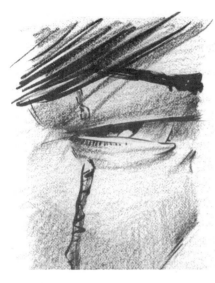

looked at the blood on his fingers.

"It's bad," he said. "I'll have a scar like. . ." and then his voice dropped off.

"Like me," Tranh finished for him.

Tranh thought back, remembering. The scar on his cheek was one of many, but it was the only one that showed. The rest were hidden . . . or in his heart.

"No, the worst scars are not like this," Tranh told him.

Beamis looked at Tranh, but the smaller boy was not looking back. Tranh was looking inside himself, thinking of his own life. He had not told Beamis much of what happened to him. In fact, he had told no one the whole story. Perhaps, he thought, it was time to reveal what he had kept hidden for so long.

"This is the only scar you can see. But there are others, inside, that are worse. You get hurt like this, on a ski hill, and you think it matters. But this is nothing – nothing – a broken leg, a scratch on your face. In a day the pain will go away; in a year you will have forgotten this, but there are things in my life I can never forget."

Beamis was staring at him with a look on his face that Tranh had not seen before.

"The scar," Beamis said. "You never told me. . ."

Tranh looked around at the fog, but he was thinking of the past. He saw water over his head. He saw the knife coming down and the water over his head, clear and green, and then red with his blood.

He should have died then. But he didn't die. He came sputtering to the surface to find that the boat filled with refugees was gone. His family was gone. His life, as he knew it, was over.

Later, another boat picked him up. It brought him to another refugee camp where he began to piece together a new life.

Beamis was still staring at the smaller boy. His eyes held a question and Tranh decided to tell him the answer.

"The scar was from a knife," Tranh said to him, reaching up to touch it. "I told you we were on a boat, and the pirates came. They were men who cared nothing about life. They came on our boat just to steal what little we had. But that was not enough for them . . ."

"What happened?" Beamis asked.

"One of them wanted my mother. He said he would kill us, unless he got what he wanted. So he began to grab her, and I tried to pull him off . . . and then the knife came down at me . . . "

Tranh was crying now, worse than Beamis in his pain. Sometimes the pain of memory was the worst pain.

"Then he threw me in the water, to die," Tranh went on. "When I came up from under the water, I could hear my mother screaming. She was crying for me and my brother and my sister. She was begging for their lives, but I could do nothing. That was the most awful thing . . . to be so close, but so powerless."

Beamis put his hand on Tranh's shoulder.

"Then her screaming stopped and they threw her body in the water. I saw. . . . I cannot forget. . . ."

The tears kept flowing down Tranh's cheeks. Beamis held him with both hands, but he could not stop the tears.

"I . . . I didn't know," Beamis said after a while.

"I have never told anyone," Tranh replied.

"Well, thank you for telling me," Beamis said.

For once, he was not joking or making fun. "You know, if they don't find us tonight, we may both be dead in the morning."

"Then I am sorry for you, my friend," Tranh said. "As for me, I died a few years ago, so I know it is not so terrible."

CHAPTER 9

Alive

The skidoos did not come until long after dark. By then, the trees and sky were black, the snow itself a dull gray under the moonlight. It was cold – well below freezing.

The rescue team was surprised by what they saw. Huddled together for warmth were the two boys – one big and brawny, one short and wiry. One of them had started a fire that had since gone out. Now there were just the two bodies, holding each other in the frozen darkness.

But they were alive.

CHAPTER 10

Miracles

Some months later, Jasmine and Tranh were at the tennis court. She was wearing a tennis dress and had a nice new racquet from her father. Tranh was dressed in cut-off jeans and worn gray running shoes. His racquet came from Goodwill and cost six dollars. One of the strings was broken, but Jasmine had said that did not matter. Here in this new country, Jasmine says, anyone can play.

Tranh took a bite of his Mr. Big bar and wondered if "anyone" included him.

"Hey, Tranh, what you eating?" they heard. It was Beamis's voice. "A chop suey bar? Pad Thai in chocolate?"

"Go suck an Egg McMuffin," Tranh yelled back.

They were both smiling. The words were rough,

but the feelings were not. In that one night on Mt. Seymour, everything had changed.

"So how come you want me to teach you this game?" Beamis asked. "I thought you were a soccer star."

"It was *her* idea," Tranh said. This was the simple truth. Jasmine's father had joined the Arbutus Club and wanted his children to play tennis. Tranh wondered about this. He thought Mr. Ling was turning away from his own culture. But Tranh would take any excuse to spend time with Jasmine. So here he was, holding his Goodwill racquet in his hand.

"Tranh, you said you wouldn't be like that," Jasmine lectured. "Tennis is fun. You should learn how to have more fun."

Tranh smiled. Jasmine always made him smile now. She thought he was too serious, but when he was with her the world seemed so much fun.

"O.K., let's get started," Beamis said. "The basic forehand grip – it's like shaking hands with the racquet..."

Tranh was not good at this, but he tried hard. He wanted to play this game, to play tennis with Jasmine and her family.

After the lesson, Jasmine and Tranh kept on hitting balls way up in the air. Many went sailing over the fence. Both he and Jasmine laughed and tried harder to control the ball, but this was not an easy game for them.

While they were playing, Buffy and Iggie came walking by the courts. Buffy had dyed her hair pink, and now called herself "Ruby" after some 1940's movie star.

"Hey, guys, what's the news?" Beamis asked. He hadn't seen them since The Breakfast Club had ended.

Buffy just shrugged. It was Iggie who did the talking.

"Not much," he said. "The only guy still in the club is Andrew. Watson kicked him out, but he keeps going anyhow. I think he's a little screwed up in the head. He's in there with Jerry, that guy who used to bug Tranh so much."

"Tell 'em about Mike," Buffy/Ruby said.

"Yeah, it's funny." Iggie told them. "Some guy came in and gave him some tests. Turns out he's a gifted kid so they sent him off to this school for gifted under-whatevers."

"Underachievers," Beamis said to help out. "I'm one of those. It's when you're real smart except you don't do anything with it."

"Yeah, then I'm one too," Iggie replied.

All of them laughed. They decided that they were all underachievers. When Iggie and Buffy went off, Beamis did a lesson on the backhand. This was even harder than the first stroke. But Tranh and Jasmine worked at it again and again. After an hour, Beamis told them he had to go.

"Sorry, guys, but I've got to get the bus. Ever since my old man took the car away, I've needed more time to get around."

"He took your car?" Jasmine asked.

"Yeah, we had a bit of an argument," Beamis said. "When it was over, there was good news and bad news. The good news was that he'd get off my case."

"The bad news was that you lost the car," Tranh finished for him.

"That's awful," Jasmine said.

"Nah," Beamis said, "it's just the price. Everything has a price. If losing a car will keep my dad off my back, it was cheap."

"Anyway, you two should keep on practicing," Beamis told them. "It takes a few weeks to get your shots in control."

"Well, thanks," Jasmine replied. "And did Tranh tell you the good news?"

"Let me guess . . . he won a year of free DVD rentals from Blockbuster."

"No!" Jasmine shouted. "This is serious. He got a phone call yesterday from a refugee agency. It's wonderful news."

Beamis looked at Tranh, his eyebrows raising up.

"My brother and sister are alive," he said. Tranh found it hard to say the words without getting tears in his eyes. "They have been in a camp since they were rescued. And all this time, they thought I died when the pirates threw me in the sea."

Jasmine took over. "There's even more good news. They're going to come to Canada as soon as Tranh's uncle can fill in the forms."

"Well, how about that?" Beamis said. "That's a real miracle, Tranh."

"Tranh deserves a few miracles," Jasmine said, smiling at her boyfriend. "He's been through an awful lot of tough stuff."

Tranh smiled as Jasmine's words washed over him. For now, for this moment, it seemed like the tough times were over.

Here are some other titles you might enjoy:

Tag Team by PAUL KROPP

Jes had plenty of problems to start with. He was short, shy and lonely – at least until he went out for the school's wrestling team. Then his life seemed to turn around – until he had to deal with Banjo and Joey down in the tunnel.

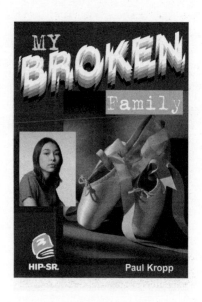

My Broken Family by PAUL KROPP

Divorce is always rotten. When Maddy's parents split up, her whole life starts to fall apart. Maddy holds on to her dancing as one thing that is really hers. But when it's all over, she finds that love is stronger than she thought.

Street Scene by **PAUL KROPP**

The guys weren't looking for trouble. Maybe Dwayne did pick the wrong girl to dance with. But did that give Sal and his gang an excuse to come after them? The fight should never have started – and it should never have finished the way it did.

Paul Kropp

HIP·SR.

Hitting the Road by PAUL KROPP

The road isn't nice to kids who run away. Matt knew there would be trouble even before he took off with his friend Cody. Along the way, there would be fighting, fear, hunger and a jump from a speeding train. Was it all worth it?

About the Author

Paul Kropp is the author of many popular novels for young people. His work includes nine award-winning young-adult novels, many high-interest novels, as well as writing for adults and younger children.

Mr. Kropp's best-known novels for young adults, *Moonkid and Prometheus* and *Moonkid and Liberty,* have been translated into German, Danish, French, Portuguese and two dialects of Spanish. They have won awards both in Canada and abroad. His most recent young-adult novels are *Running the Bases* and *Homerun.*

Paul Kropp lives with his wife, Lori Jamison, in an 1889 townhouse in Toronto's Cabbagetown district.

**For more information, see the author's website at
www.paulkropp.com**

For more information on HIP books, go to the website:

 High Interest Publishing – Publishers of H•I•P Books
www.hip-books.com